200 QUESTIONS A[BOUT]
AMERICAN HISTORY

Student Book

Compiled by Sean Brooks

MEMORIA PRESS
www.MemoriaPress.com

200 QUESTIONS ABOUT AMERICAN HISTORY

STUDENT BOOK
Compiled by Sean Brooks

ISBN 978-1-61538-109-8

© 2012 Memoria Press 0817

Cover illustration by Jean Leon Gerome Ferris, 1921

CONTENTS

Recommended Texts & Weekly Schedule

The Story of the Thirteen Colonies & the Great Republic (Noted as **Guerber** below) by H. A. Guerber, edited by Memoria Press

Story of the World, Volume 4 (Noted as **SOTW** below) by Susan Wise Bauer

This guide previously utilized information from *Everything You Need to Know About American History Homework* by Anne Zeman and Kate Kelly, which has gone out of print. Most of the facts, dates, and quotes in this guide can still be found in either Guerber or *Story of the World*, but a few are not included in these books. We left them in this guide because they are important aspects of American history and can easily be found in other sources.

Week	Reading Selections		Drill Questions	Time-line	Quotes	Presidents
1	Guerber	Chapters 1-7	1-8	1		
2		Chapters 8-14	9-16			
3		Chapters 15-21	17-24			
4		Chapters 22-28	25-28	2		
5	REVIEW FOR TEST					
6	TEST I					
7	Guerber	Chapters 29-33	29-40	3-7	1-2	
8		Chapters 34-38	41-46	8	3	
9		Chapters 39-43	47-52	9	4-5	
10	REVIEW FOR TEST					
11	TEST II					
12	Guerber	Chapters 44-47	53-59	10		1-5
13		Chapters 48-52	60-66	11	6	Quiz
14		Chapters 53-56	67-72	12-13	7-9	6-10
15		Chapters 57-61	73-79		10-11	Quiz
16	REVIEW FOR TEST					
17	TEST					11-15
18	Guerber	Chapters 62-66	80-94	14-15	12-13	Quiz
19		Chapters 67-70	95-100	16	14	16-20
20		Chapters 71-74	101-103	17		Quiz
21		Chapters 75-78	104-107	18-19		21-25
22	REVIEW FOR TEST					Quiz
23	TEST					

24	Guerber	Chapters 79-85	108-116	20	15-16	26-30
25	SOTW	pp. 216-222, 227-232, 245-256	117-122	21-22		Quiz
26	SOTW	pp. 260-272, 281-290	123-127	23	17	31-35
27	REVIEW FOR TEST					Quiz
28	TEST					
29	SOTW	pp. 299-316, 317-322	128-135	24-25		36-40
30	SOTW	pp. 322-327, 345-350, 367-372	136-140	26-29		Quiz
31	SOTW	pp. 385-401	141-144		18-19	41-44
32	SOTW	pp. 402-414, 449-451, 459-464	145-150	30	20	
33	REVIEW FOR TEST					Final Test
34	FINAL EXAM					

*Quotes 16, 17, and 20 are not noted in Gurber or SOTW.

Teaching Guidelines

☐ Read the assigned chapters from the text (*The Story of the Thirteen Colonies & the Great Republic* or *Story of the World, Volume 4*). Have student(s) read aloud.

☐ Make sure to take time to stop and discuss interesting events or people.

☐ Complete the questions found in the *200 Questions About American History* workbook corresponding to the chapters that have been read (see schedule on facing page and above).

☐ Review daily, if possible, the facts that have been learned up to this point.

☐ Take tests as scheduled.

DRILL QUESTIONS

1. The original inhabitants of this continent: (Guerber Ch. 1)

   _____

2. The Viking credited as the first European to visit North America in 1000 AD:
   (Guerber Ch. 2) _____

   What did he name it?_____

3. King of Portugal who suggested it was possible to sail around Africa: (Guerber Ch. 3)

   _____

4. Financed Columbus's first voyage: (Guerber Ch. 4)

   _____

5. European credited with the discovery of America: (Guerber Chs. 5-6)

   _____

6. English sailor who discovered Cape Cod: (Guerber Ch. 7)

   _____

7. First European to reach India by sea: (Guerber Ch. 7)

   _____

8. Explorer after whom our continent is named: (Guerber Ch. 7)

   _____

9. Leader of the first expedition to circle the globe: (Guerber Ch. 8)

   _____

10. French sailor who discovered the St. Lawrence River: (Guerber Ch. 9)

    _____

11. Oldest city in the mainland of the United States: (Guerber Ch. 9)

    _____

12. First English sailor to circle the globe: (Guerber Ch. 10)

    _____

13. First English colony in America, which disappeared: (Guerber Ch. 11)

    _____

    Who established the colony? _____

14. First lasting English colony: (Guerber Chs. 12-3)

    _____

15. Head of the colony in Jamestown: (Guerber Ch. 12)

    _____

16. First form of representative government in America, established in Virginia:
    (Guerber Ch. 13) _____

17. Englishmen who desired a plainer and purer religion:

(Guerber Ch. 15) _____

Puritans that left the Anglican Church altogether: _____

Separatists that sailed to the new land: _____

18. The agreement that established a form of government for the Pilgrims:

(Guerber Ch. 16) _____

19. Native Americans who aided the Pilgrims: (Guerber Ch. 16)

_____

20. Law that forbade colonists from building boats and required all goods to be

carried on English ships: (Guerber Ch. 19) _____

21. Protector of England who established the Navigation Act: (Guerber Ch.19)

_____

22. Land purchased by the Dutch man Minuit for about twenty-four dollars' worth of trinkets:

(Guerber Ch. 20) _____

23. Land granted to William Penn: (Guerber Ch. 21) _____

24. Borderline separating Pennsylvania and Maryland: (Guerber Ch. 21)

_____

25. Short civil war in Virginia during which Jamestown was seized: (Guerber Ch. 22)

_____

26. War between France and England (Guerber Ch. 25, 28-29)

In America: _____

In Europe: _____

27. General who captured Quebec: (Guerber Ch. 28)

_____

28. Document that signified the end of the French and Indian War: (Guerber Ch. 28)

_____

29. Chief frustration of American colonists: (Guerber Ch. 30)

_____

30. Five causes of the Revolutionary War: (Guerber Chs. 29-30)

1. _____

2. _____

3. _____

4. _____

5. _____

31. Event in Boston during which British soldiers opened fire on unarmed colonists:

(Guerber Ch. 30) _____

32. Event during which Americans dressed as natives and dumped tea in the harbor: (Guerber Ch. 30) _____

33. First time delegates from all the colonies met to discuss the rights of American colonists: (Guerber Ch. 30) _____

34. Volunteer soldiers ready at a moment's notice: (Guerber Ch. 30)

   _____

35. Riders sent to warn Charlestown and Lexington of the coming British army: (Guerber Ch. 31) _____

36. First battles of the Revolutionary War: (Guerber Ch. 31)

   _____

37. R. W. Emerson describes the first battle as: (Guerber Ch. 32)

   _____

38. Commander-in-chief of the Continental Army: (Guerber Ch. 32)

   _____

39. Revolutionary battle lost by Americans but considered a victory: (Guerber Ch. 32)

   _____

40. General at Bunker Hill: (Guerber Ch. 32) _____

41. Father of the Declaration of Independence: (Guerber Ch. 34)

   _____

42. President of Congress that accepted the Declaration: (Guerber Ch. 34)

   _____

43. The young American patriot who was hanged as a spy by the British (Guerber Ch. 35) _____

44. Event during which Washington surprised and captured the Hessians: (Guerber Ch. 35) _____

45. French nobleman who served in the American army: (Guerber Ch. 36)

   _____

46. Battle that was the turning point for the Revolutionary War: (Guerber Ch. 37)

   _____

47. American naval officer who did great damage to the British navy during the Revolutionary War: (Guerber Ch. 39)_____

48. Traitor who plotted to give up the fort at West Point: (Guerber Ch. 41)

   _____

49. Final battle of the Revolutionary War: (Guerber Ch. 42) _____

50. British general forced to surrender at Yorktown: (Guerber Ch. 42)

   _____

51. Document that signified the official end of the Revolutionary War: (Guerber Ch. 42)

    _____

52. Name the thirteen original colonies: (Guerber Ch. 43)

    1. _____   8. _____

    2. _____   9. _____

    3. _____   10. _____

    4. _____   11. _____

    5. _____   12. _____

    6. _____   13. _____

    7. _____

53. Document that established a central government for the United States:
    (Guerber Ch. 44) _____

54. Revolt that demonstrated the need for a stronger central government:
    (Guerber Ch. 44) _____

55. Framework for the government of the United States: (Guerber Ch. 45)

    _____

56. Father of the Constitution: (Guerber Ch. 45)

    _____

57. Three branches of the American government established by the Constitution:
    (Guerber Ch. 45)

    1. Law-making branch: _____

       Head of the law-making branch: _____

       Two bodies of Congress: _____

    2. Law-enforcing branch: _____

       Head of the law-enforcing branch: _____

    3. Law-interpreting branch: _____

       Head of the law-interpreting branch: _____

       Head of the Supreme Court: _____

58. First president of the United States: (Guerber Ch. 46)

    _____

59. First Chief Justice of the Supreme Court: (Guerber Ch. 46)

    _____

60. Inventor of the cotton gin: (Guerber Ch. 48)

    _____

61. United States national motto and meaning: (Guerber Ch. 50)

    _____

62. Land purchased by Jefferson from Emperor Napoleon:
(Guerber Ch. 50) _____

63. Men hired by Jefferson to explore the new territory: (Guerber Ch. 50)

_____

64. Inventor of the first steamboat: (Guerber Ch. 51)_____

65. Native chief who led war against settlers in the Indiana Territory: (Guerber Ch. 52)

_____

66. Governor of the Indiana Territory who defeated the feared Native chief:
(Guerber Ch. 52) _____

67. War fought to free American trade and earn the respect of other nations:
(Guerber Ch. 53 & 55)_____

68. Famous American naval officers who fought in the War of 1812: (Guerber Ch. 54)

_____

69. Wrote "The Star-Spangled Banner" while held captive on a British ship:
(Guerber Ch. 55) _____

70. Document that signified the end of the War of 1812: (Guerber Ch. 55)

_____

71. Battle fought after the War of 1812 had ended: (Guerber Ch. 55)

_____

72. American general at the Battle of New Orleans: (Guerber Ch. 55)

_____

73. Foreign policy that forbade European countries from establishing colonies in
North or South America and told them not to meddle in American affairs:
(Guerber Ch. 57) _____

74. Law that inducted Maine into the Union as a free state and Missouri as a slave
state and said no slavery will be allowed in the Louisiana Territory above the 36°
30° parallel: (Guerber Ch. 57) _____

75. Law passed by South Carolina in reaction to Congress' attempt to place a high
tariff on foreign goods: (Guerber Ch. 58) _____

76. Invention that changed modern agriculture: (Guerber Ch. 59)

_____

77. Those who opposed slavery: (Guerber Ch. 61)

_____

78. Wrote the first dictionary in America: (Guerber Ch. 61)

_____

79. Inventor of the telegraph: (Guerber Ch. 61) _____

80. Battle during which one hundred fifty Texans fought a Mexican army of four thousand: (Guerber Ch. 62) _____

81. Name three heroes that helped lead Texas to independence: (Guerber Ch. 62)

    _____

82. War fought over the boundaries between Texas and Mexico: (Guerber Ch. 62)

    _____

83. General of the Mexican army: (Guerber Ch. 62)

    _____

84. American general who defeated Santa Anna: (Guerber Ch. 62)

    _____

85. American general who captured Mexico City: (Guerber Ch. 62)

    _____

86. American pioneer who conquered California: (Guerber Ch. 62 & 63)

    _____

87. Treaty that ended the Mexican-American War and gave the United States New Mexico and what was called Upper California: (Guerber Ch. 63)

    _____

88. Land purchased from Mexico in the West for building train routes to California: (Guerber Ch. 63) _____

89. Massachusetts Senator known as one of the greatest orators in the history of the U.S.: (Guerber Ch. 63) _____

90. Movement of many settlers to California in hopes of becoming rich: (Guerber Ch. 64)

    _____

91. Bill that inducted California as a free state and allowed the Utah and New Mexico territories to choose whether or not they would be free or slave states: (Guerber Ch. 65)

    _____

92. System of secretly transporting slaves to Canada: (Guerber Ch. 65)

    _____

93. Former slave who led over 300 slaves to freedom: (Guerber Ch. 65)

    _____

94. Author of *Uncle Tom's Cabin*: (Guerber Ch. 66)

    _____

95. Slave who appealed to the Supreme Court for his freedom: (Guerber Ch. 67)

    _____

96. First state to secede from the Union: (Guerber Ch. 69)

_____

97. Government established by the states that seceded from the Union: (Guerber Ch. 69)

_____

98. President of the Confederacy: (Guerber Ch. 69)

_____

99. States in the Confederacy: (Guerber Ch. 69-70)

    1. _____   7. _____
    2. _____   8. _____
    3. _____   9. _____
    4. _____   10. _____
    5. _____   11. _____
    6. _____

100. Location of the first shot fired in the Civil War: (Guerber Ch. 69)

_____

101. Confederate ironclad ship that wrought havoc on the Union fleet: (Guerber Ch. 72)

_____

Union ironclad that defeated the Confederate ironclad: _____

102. Commander-in-chief of the Confederate Army: (Guerber Ch. 73)

_____

103. Act of President Lincoln that declared all slaves free in the Confederate States:
(Guerber Ch. 74)

_____

104. Battle that changed the course of the Civil War: (Guerber Ch. 75)

_____

105. Commander-in-chief of the Union Army: (Guerber Ch. 76)

_____

106. Union general who captured and burned Atlanta: (Guerber Ch. 76)

_____

107. Place where Lee surrendered to Grant: (Guerber Ch. 78)

_____

108. Actor who assassinated President Lincoln: (Guerber Ch. 79)

_____

109. Men from the North who took office in the South without having land in the South:
(Guerber Ch. 80) _____

Men who were willing to vote for anyone who paid them: _____

110. General who fought the Sioux at Big Horn: (Guerber Ch. 82)

_____

111. Inventor of the electric lightbulb: (Guerber Ch. 82)

_____

Inventor of the telephone: _____

112. Gift France presented to the U.S. during the presidency of Grover Cleveland:
(Guerber Ch. 84) _____

113. Event that led to America declaring war with Spain: (Guerber Ch. 85)

_____

114. War that forced Spain to give up all control of Cuba, Puerto Rico, and the
Philippines: (Guerber Ch. 85)_____

115. The original name given to WWI: (SOTW p. 216)

_____

116. Archduke of Austria-Hungary killed by a Serbian revolutionary: (SOTW p. 217)

_____

_____

117. Two competing forces in WWI: (SOTW p. 219)
Allies: _____

_____

_____

Central Powers: _____

_____

_____

118. President during WWI: (SOTW p. 227)

_____

119. The right of women to vote: (SOTW p. 231)

_____

120. The three men who met together to draft the peace treaty after WWI and the
countries they represented: (SOTW p. 245)

1. _____

2. _____

3. _____

121. Harsh document drafted at the peace conference after WWI: (SOTW p. 247)

_____

122. Wilson's idea for sustained world peace: (SOTW p. 246)

_____

123. Event that bankrupted the American economy, culminating in Black Tuesday: (SOTW p. 283)

_____

124. Era of hardship initiated by the Stock Market Crash (or Wall Street Crash): (SOTW p. 284)

_____

125. President Franklin D. Roosevelt's Federal aid programs, begun as an answer to the Great Depression: (SOTW p. 285) _____

126. Axis dictators at the beginning of WWII:

Soviet Union: (SOTW p. 252) _____

Italy: (SOTW p. 263) _____

Japan: (SOTW p. 270) _____

Germany: (SOTW p. 287) _____

127. National Socialist German Workers' Party: (SOTW pp. 289-90)

_____

128. Event that started WWII: (SOTW p. 302)

_____

129. Event that led America to join WWII: (SOTW p. 308)

_____

130. President Roosevelt described the attack on Pearl Harbor as: (SOTW p. 308)

_____

131. Two competing forces in WWII: (SOTW pp. 302, 305, 317, & 320)

Allies: _____

_____

_____

Axis Powers: _____

_____

_____

132. Systematic extermination of European Jews by the Nazis: (SOTW p. 312)

_____

133. British prime minister who refused to give in to Nazi attacks during WWII: (SOTW p. 318) _____

134. The largest land assault during WWII, also called D-Day: (SOTW p. 321)

_____

135. American general and commander of the Allied forces who organized D-Day: (SOTW p. 321) _____

136. Top secret project intended to create an atomic bomb: (SOTW p. 325)

_____

American scientist in charge of the project: _____

137. Two Japanese cities destroyed by the first atomic bombs: (SOTW pp. 323, 326)

_____

138. Organization of nations created to keep the peace after WWII: (SOTW p. 327)

_____

139. Plan to use U.S. money to fund the reconstruction of Western Europe: (SOTW p. 347)

_____

140. War fought against the Soviet Union's attempt to expand their influence south of the 38th parallel: (SOTW p. 368-369) _____

141. Longstanding conflict between the spread of communism by the Soviet Union and the sustaining of democracy: (SOTW p. 386)

_____

142. First astronauts to set foot on the moon: (SOTW pp. 387-88)

_____

143. Event during Cold War in which the United States and the Soviet Union almost engaged in nuclear war: (SOTW pp. 394-95)

_____

144. President who fought to put America ahead in the "Space Race" and was assassinated while in Texas: (SOTW p. 399)

_____

145. Laws in America that enforced the segregation of races: (SOTW p. 402)

_____

146. The movement of protest in America against the unjust laws of segregation: (SOTW p. 403)

_____

147. African American woman arrested for occupying a white man's bus seat: (SOTW p. 404)

_____

148. Minister who led the Civil Rights Movement through non-violent protest: (SOTW p. 406)

_____

149. The second major conflict fought during the Cold War: (SOTW p. 411-412)

_____

150. Event that demonstrated the end of communist rule in Europe and signified the end of the Cold War: (SOTW p. 461)

_____

TIMELINE OF AMERICAN HISTORY

1. _____ Columbus discovered America (Guerber Ch. 5)

2. _____ French and Indian War (Guerber Ch. 25, 28)

3. _____ Boston Massacre (Guerber Ch. 30)

4. _____ Boston Tea Party (Guerber Ch. 30)

5. _____ First Continental Congress (Guerber Ch. 30)

6. _____ Battles of Lexington and Concord (Guerber Ch. 31)

7. _____ Second Continental Congress (Guerber Ch. 32)

8. _____ Declaration of Independence (Guerber Ch. 34)

9. _____ Second Treaty of Paris (Guerber Ch. 42)

10. _____ The Constitution (Guerber Ch. 46)

11. _____ Louisiana Purchase (Guerber Ch. 50)

12. _____ War of 1812 (Guerber Ch. 53, 55)

13. _____ Treaty of Ghent (Guerber Ch. 55)

14. _____ The Mexican-American War (Guerber Ch. 62)

15. _____ Gold Rush (Guerber Ch. 64)

16. _____ Battle at Fort Sumter (Guerber Ch. 69)

17. _____ Emancipation Proclamation (Guerber Ch. 74)

18. _____ Battle of Gettysburg (Guerber Ch. 75)

19. _____ surrender at Appomattox (Guerber Ch. 78)

20. _____ The Spanish-American War (Guerber Ch. 85)

21. _____ America enters WWI (SOTW p. 221)

22. _____ WWI (The Great War) (SOTW pp. 219, 230)

23. _____ The Great Depression (SOTW p. 284)

24. _____ Nazis invade Poland (SOTW p. 302)

25. _____ attack on Pearl Harbor (SOTW p. 307)

26. _____ European Theater of WWII ends (V-E Day) (SOTW p. 322)

27. _____ Pacific Theater of WWII ends (V-J Day)

28. _____ The Cold War (SOTW pp. 449-450, 452)

29. _____ The Korean War (SOTW pp. 369-70)

30. _____ The Vietnam War (SOTW pp. 411-414)

NOTABLE QUOTES FROM AMERICAN HISTORY

1. *"I know not what course others may take; but as for me, give me liberty or give me death!"*

    Who said it? (Guerber Ch. 30) _____

2. *"Don't fire until you see the whites of their eyes!"*

    Who said it? (Guerber Ch. 32) _____

    What was the occasion? _____

3. *"I only regret that I have but one life to lose for my country."*

    Who said it? (Guerber Ch. 35) _____

4. *"I have not yet begun to fight."*

    Who said it? (Guerber Ch. 39) _____

    What was the occasion? _____

5. *"That man has an ax to grind."*

    Who said it? (Guerber Ch. 43) _____

6. *"To be prepared for war is one of the most effectual means of preserving peace."*

    Who said it? (Guerber Ch. 49) _____

7. *"Don't give up the ship!"*

    Who said it? (Guerber Ch. 54) _____

    What was the occasion? _____

8. *"We have met the enemy and they are ours."*

    Who said it? (Guerber Ch. 54) _____

    What was the occasion? _____

9. *"Perhaps so; but I shall have the honor of presiding at that dinner."*

    Who said it? (Guerber Ch. 55) _____

    What was the occasion? _____

    _____

10. *"To the victors belong the spoils."*

    Who said it? (Guerber Ch. 58) _____

    What was the occasion? _____

    _____

11. *"Liberty and Union, now and forever, one and inseparable."*

    Who said it? (Guerber Ch. 58) _____

12. *"Be sure you are right, then go ahead."*

    Who said it? (Guerber Ch. 62) _____

13. *"Slavery is in all probability the wedge which will split up this union."*

    Who said it? (Guerber Ch. 63) _____

14. *"If I can ever hit that thing, I'll hit it hard!"*

    Who said it? (Guerber Ch. 68) _____

    What was the occasion? _____

15. *"Sic semper tyrannis!"*

    Who said it? (Guerber Ch. 79) _____

    What was the occasion? _____

16. *"Speak softly and carry a big stick."*

    Who said it? _____

17. *"The only thing we have to fear is fear itself."*

    Who said it? _____

18. *"That's one small step for a man, one giant leap for mankind."*

    Who said it? (SOTW p. 388) _____

    What was the occasion? _____

19. *"Ask not what your country can do for you—ask what you can do for your country."*

    Who said it? (SOTW p. 402) _____

20. "I have a dream ..."

    Who said it? _____

    What was the occasion? _____

PRESIDENTS OF THE UNITED STATES

1. _____ first president of the United States

2. _____ signed the Declaration of Independence

3. _____ president who purchased Louisiana

4. _____ president during War of 1812

5. _____ author of the Monroe Doctrine

6. _____ president during completion of the Erie Canal

7. _____ resided during Nullification Act and the Alamo

8. _____ president during Panic of 1837

9. _____ general known as "Old Tippecanoe"

10. _____ president when Texas was added to the Union

11. _____ president during the Mexican War

12. _____ general who captured Mexico City

13. _____ president during Compromise of 1850

14. _____ completed Gadsden Purchase

15. _____ president during Dred Scott court case

16. _____ president during the Civil War

17. _____ first president to be impeached

18. _____ general-in-chief during the Civil War

19. _____ pulled Union troops out of South

20. _____ shot by disgruntled office-seekers

21. _____ president when "Spoils System" ended

22. _____ resided during dedication of the Statue of Liberty

23. _____ grandson of "Old Tippecanoe"

24. _____ only president to serve two non-consecutive terms

25. _____ president during the Spanish-American War

26. _____ his policies were known as "the Square Deal"

27. _____ supported the start of income tax

28. _____ president during WWI

29. _____ considered one of the weakest presidents of the U.S.

30. _____ quiet man; referred to as "Silent Cal"

31. _____ president during Stock Market Crash

32. _____ proposed the "New Deal" and resided during WWII

33. _____ president during the beginning of the Cold War

34. _____ general who orchestrated D-Day during WWII

35. _____ president during building of the Berlin Wall

36. _____ president during Vietnam War

37. _____ involved in the Watergate Scandal

38. _____ only man to become president without being elected

39. _____ president who negotiated peace between Israel and Egypt

40. _____ received the most electoral votes of any president

41. _____ president during fall of the Berlin Wall

42. _____ second president to be impeached

43. _____ president during the attacks on the Twin Towers

44. _____ first African-American president

45. _____ our current president

The Star-Spangled Banner

O! say can you see by the dawn's early light

What so proudly we hailed at the twilight's last gleaming?

Whose broad stripes and bright stars through the perilous fight,

O'er the ramparts we watched were so gallantly streaming?

And the rockets' red glare, the bombs bursting in air,

Gave proof through the night that our flag was still there.

O! say does that star-spangled banner yet wave

O'er the land of the free and the home of the brave?

On the shore, dimly seen through the mists of the deep,

Where the foe's haughty host in dread silence reposes,

What is that which the breeze, o'er the towering steep,

As it fitfully blows, half conceals, half discloses?

Now it catches the gleam of the morning's first beam,

In full glory reflected now shines in the stream:

'Tis the star-spangled banner! Oh long may it wave

O'er the land of the free and the home of the brave.

And where is that band who so vauntingly swore

That the havoc of war and the battle's confusion,

A home and a country should leave us no more!

Their blood has washed out their foul footsteps' pollution.

No refuge could save the hireling and slave

From the terror of flight, or the gloom of the grave:

And the star-spangled banner in triumph doth wave

O'er the land of the free and the home of the brave.

O! thus be it ever, when freemen shall stand

Between their loved home and the war's desolation!

Blest with victory and peace, may the heav'n rescued land

Praise the Power that hath made and preserved us a nation.

Then conquer we must, when our cause it is just,

And this be our motto: 'In God is our trust.'

And the star-spangled banner in triumph shall wave

O'er the land of the free and the home of the brave!

—Francis Scott Key

Old Ironsides

Ay, tear her tattered ensign down!

Long has it waved on high,

And many an eye has danced to see

That banner in the sky;

Beneath it rung the battle shout,

And burst the cannon's roar;

The meteor of the ocean air

Shall sweep the clouds no more.

Her deck, once red with heroes' blood,

Where knelt the vanquished foe,

When winds were hurrying o'er the flood,

And waves were white below,

No more shall feel the victor's tread,

Or know the conquered knee;

The harpies of the shore shall pluck

The eagle of the sea!

Oh, better that her shattered bulk

Should sink beneath the wave;

Her thunders shook the mighty deep,

And there should be her grave;

Nail to the mast her holy flag,

Set every threadbare sail,

And give her to the god of storms,

The lightning and the gale!

—Oliver Wendell Holmes

O Captain! My Captain!

O Captain! my Captain! our fearful trip is done;

The ship has weather'd every rack, the prize we sought is won;

The port is near, the bells I hear, the people all exulting,

While follow eyes the steady keel, the vessel grim and daring:

But O heart! heart! heart!

O the bleeding drops of red,

Where on the deck my Captain lies,

Fallen cold and dead.

O Captain! my Captain! rise up and hear the bells;

Rise up—for you the flag is flung—for you the bugle trills;

For you bouquets and ribbon'd wreaths—for you the shores a-crowding;

For you they call, the swaying mass, their eager faces turning;

Here Captain! dear father!

This arm beneath your head;

It is some dream that on the deck,

You've fallen cold and dead.

My Captain does not answer, his lips are pale and still;

My father does not feel my arm, he has no pulse nor will;

The ship is anchor'd safe and sound, its voyage closed and done;

From fearful trip, the victor ship, comes in with object won;

Exult, O shores, and ring, O bells!

But I, with mournful tread,

Walk the deck my Captain lies,

Fallen cold and dead.

—Walt Whitman